My Sister

Joanna Young

Who knows you the best ...

and laughs at your jokes?

Who is the one who
sits **next** to you ...

grows up with you ...

and is **always** on your side?

Who knows how to **play** ...

helps you up
when you are down ...

and keeps your
secrets safe?

Who **protects** you ...

shares with you ...

and shows you the way?

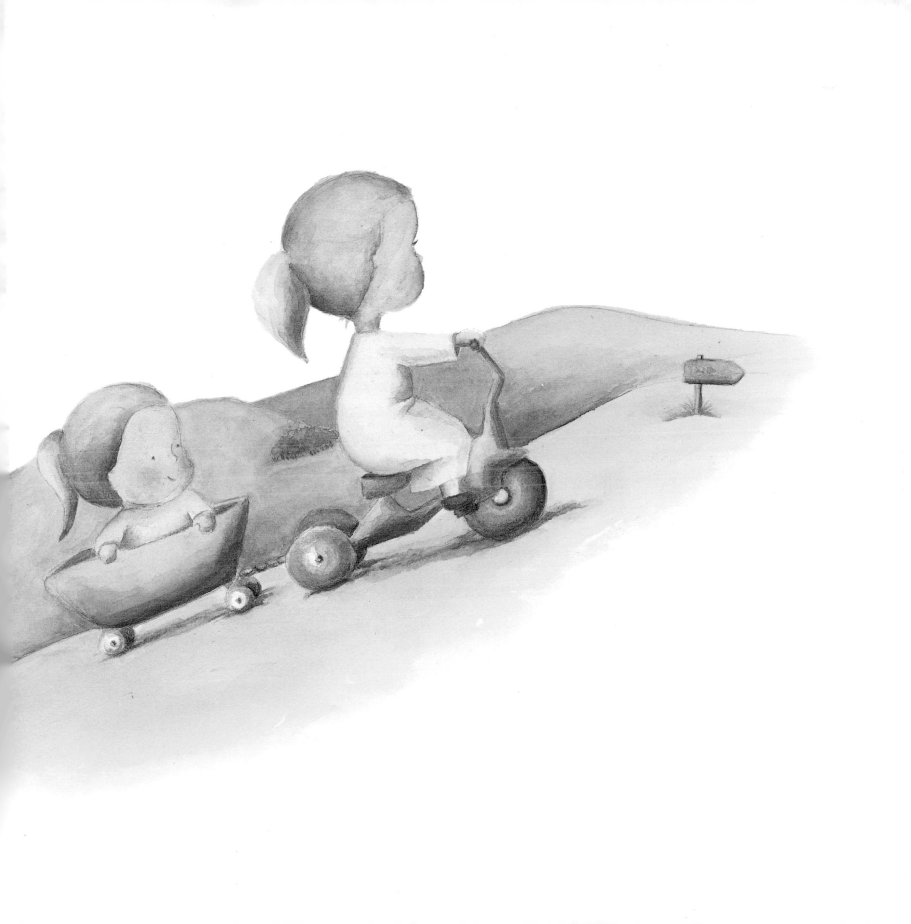

Who takes **care** of you ...

and loves you back?

Your sister,
that's who!

For my sister Tess, who inspired this book,
and for my babies Georgia and Tabatha,
whose sunshine and curiosity helped me
believe in it.

First published 2015 by Wild Hare Books.
Published in the UK in 2018
by New Frontier Publishing Europe Ltd
93 Harbord Street, London SW6 6PN
www.newfrontierpublishing.co.uk

ISBN: 978 1 912076 51 2 (HB)

A CIP catalogue record for this book is available from
the British Library.

Designed by Celeste Hulme

Printed in China
10 9 8 7 6 5 4 3 2 1